365

ways to feel AMAZING

365 WAYS TO FEEL AMAZING

An Hachette UK Company
www.hachette.co.uk

Vie Books, an imprint of Summersdale Publishers Ltd
Part of Octopus Publishing Group Limited
Carmelite House
50 Victoria Embankment
LONDON
EC4Y 0DZ
UK

www.summersdale.com

Printed and bound in the Czech Republic

ISBN: 978-1-78685-769-9

Substantial discounts on bulk quantities of Summersdale books are available to corporations, professional associations and other organisations. For details contact general enquiries: telephone: +44 (0) 1243 771107 or email: enquiries@summersdale.com.

Neither the author nor the publisher can be held responsible for any loss or claim arising out of the use, or misuse, of the suggestions made herein. Consult your doctor before undertaking any new forms of exercise.

365

vie ways to feel AMAZING

Be yourself! No matter how many of the following changes you incorporate into your lifestyle, stay true to your values and share them with the world. Remember to always be proud of who you are.

2

Blend a smoothie using a banana and lots of berries, then sneak in a handful of spinach. You won't taste it, but spinach is rich in magnesium – a natural muscle relaxant and stress-reducer – and it will leave you feeling calmer.

3

There's a reason avocados are so popular – not only are they delicious, but their benefits also include protecting your heart and helping with digestion. Also, as a natural hormone balancer, they could even improve your mood.

It's hard to resist a perfectly ripe strawberry, and in this case you should give in to temptation. These berries are rich in vitamins and serve as a strong defence against brain degeneration.

Try to squeeze in 5–10 minutes of jumping jacks – a 68 kg (150 lbs) woman can burn 90 calories in just one 10-minute session, and you'll boost your endorphins, which will give you an instant mood boost.

Next time you go out for cocktails, try giving some of the mocktails a go instead; often they mimic the taste of the alcoholic version, they won't leave you with any unpleasant side effects, and they cost less!

7

We all love snacks at the cinema, but this can lead to mindless eating and end up lowering your mood. Studies have shown that picking up food with your non-dominant hand can make you more mindful of what you eat.

8

Stay hydrated. Around 6–8 glasses of water a day is recommended to avoid dehydration and fatigue. Give your body the water it needs to feel fresh and perky.

Clear out some clutter that you no longer use.
A tidy home means a tidy mind, so this small act
can help you de-stress – plus you can donate your
unwanted items to charity for others to enjoy.

Buying a new gadget or some new clothes can give you a burst
of pleasure, but why not donate the money that you would
have spent on this to a charity that's close to your heart?

Volunteer for something you care about in your local area. Putting yourself forward for a local community project, such as cleaning up a neighbourhood park or helping out in a food bank, is a great use of your time and you'll be making a positive impact on the world around you.

12

It's always nice to get presents on your birthday, but if there's nothing you really want then ask your loved ones to donate to your chosen charity – making others happy is sure to make for a great gift.

13

Donate surplus food to a local food bank. Many of us are fortunate enough to have plenty of food at our fingertips, but not everyone is so lucky – make sure to help those in need when you can.

14

Volunteer in a local homeless shelter or soup kitchen; helping out those who are less fortunate than you is a great way to connect with people from different walks of life and appreciate what you have yourself.

15

Create a care package for a friend who is sick or in need of a pick-me-up: chocolate, tea, flowers, reading material and other comforting treats work wonders. The recipient will be touched by your thoughtfulness and delighted by the surprise.

16

Make time for a massage. Many of us spend too long hunched over a desk or always on the go. Take some time out to have a proper massage to ease your muscles and unwind your mind.

Bake some sweet treats and share them
with your friends and colleagues –
you'll be everyone's hero for the day!

18

Deck out your desk space. A desk can often be
associated with worry and stress, but try giving
yours a makeover. Buy a plant – real or fake –
or put up some of your favourite pictures.

Make a to-do list – this will add
structure to your day, and crossing
things off as you go will feel great.

20

Many of us tend to shrink into ourselves in social and business environments, so try performing some power poses beforehand. Standing tall with your hands on your hips has been shown to positively influence your mood and attitude.

21

Make the most of your commute. Many of us waste hours of time scrolling through our phones on the way to work. Take along a good book or listen to an engaging podcast to make the best use of those weekday mornings and evenings.

Many of us don't have the amount or quality of sleep required for a positive mindset. Invest in some aromatherapy oils or have an aromatherapy session to help reduce anxiety and induce better sleep.

Create a sleep sanctuary for yourself. For a truly restful night's sleep, aim to make your bedroom pleasantly cool (around 16°C or 61°F) and free from any intrusive noise or light.

24 Take a magnesium supplement half an hour before you go to bed – this should decrease the time it takes to fall asleep, as well as increase the quality and length of your rest.

Let dawn wake you up. Leave your curtains or blinds open – or put a lamp on a timer to switch on 15 minutes before your alarm goes off to create a 'dawn simulation' effect. Brightening your bedroom when you wake has been shown to make you feel happier throughout the day! **25**

If you find that light or noise at night is disrupting your sleep, experiment with a sleeping mask or earplugs.

Another way of reducing distractions is to use a white noise machine or app to listen to soothing sounds – wind, surf, steam, rain – as these will help you zone out and drift off.

To help you fall asleep, listen to ambient music – what's important is that there are no dramatic shifts in the dynamics of the music.

29

Having the right bedding is key to a good night's sleep. To choose the perfect pillow, consider your size, sleeping position and preference. If you fold your pillow in half and it doesn't spring open, replace it!

30

Try certain foods for restful sleep – foods like turkey and warm milk (containing tryptophan) can help you produce melatonin, which is the hormone that helps us sleep. Almonds, camomile tea and oatcakes may also help.

31

When you live close to family, friends or a partner, it can be easy to take out your stresses on each other. Allow yourself to have your own space and vent frustrations through exercise.

32

Mindfulness is important in helping you take stock of yourself and focus on the present moment. Download a free mindfulness app to help you fit in a few minutes a day.

33

It's easy to book yourself up with work and social events, but make sure you set aside some time for self-care, as this can vastly improve your mood in the long run.

Most of us spend a lot of time on our phones – try leaving your technology behind when you head out sometimes. Scroll through memories in your head rather than status updates on a screen.

34

35

Consider a general digital detox. We live in an age of non-stop information, which can be overwhelming. Try turning off your devices for increasingly longer periods of time: an hour, an evening, a weekend, etc.

Going barefoot is a tactile treat and it's the perfect opportunity to practise mindfulness. Spend a day barefoot at home and enjoy being aware of the texture and temperature beneath your feet.

36

37

Don't bottle things up. Talk to a friend or partner when you're feeling low – even if they just listen, you'll feel much lighter and more at ease afterwards.

Build trust. Trust is the foundation of any close relationship, romantic or otherwise. By building trust and being honest with people around you, you will have deeper and longer lasting connections.

39

Be the friend you'd love to have. By being the best friend you can be, you're more likely to draw great people to you, and to have your friends treat you with mutual love and support.

40

Spend time with upbeat, supportive people; their positivity will rub off on you and put you in an optimistic frame of mind.

41

Make a list of what you are most thankful for – feel genuine gratitude for simple things like the hot meal you are about to eat or being surrounded by loving family and friends.

42

Celebrate individuality, in yourself and others. We are all so different, and that is a wonderful thing. Embrace the things that make you unique, and support others in doing the same. Whether it's your sense of humour or a friend's sartorial style, take a moment to show some love.

Cherish the compliments you receive. Take a moment to internalise what has been said and say a genuine thank you to the person who gave it to you.

43

44

Smile! This simple act releases endorphins, the feel-good chemical in our bodies – and studies have shown that a person's mood will reflect the emotion that their face is communicating.

Accept yourself as you are – many of us are constantly striving towards the 'perfect body'. There's no problem with self-improvement, but remember to value and cherish your body whatever it weighs or looks like right now.

45

46

Try standing in front of the mirror and repeating some positive mantras. Saying something as simple as 'I am enough' can have a big impact on your mindset as you go about the day.

Learn something new. Whether it's taking driving lessons, learning another language or pursuing a new hobby, becoming skilled at something new is sure to boost your self-esteem.

47

48

Neutralise negative thinking. No one can be positive all the time, but it's good to be aware of any negativity creeping in. Catch negative thoughts and dismiss them calmly to attain an optimistic outlook.

49

Don't sweat the small stuff. Whenever you find yourself worrying about trivial things, think realistically about the worst-case scenario and how unlikely that is.

50

Feeling overwhelmed? Visualise all of your worries and thoughts as different objects – then put each one in a different box and open one box at a time when you are ready to deal with it.

51

If you're lucky enough to live near the sea, get down there, kick off your shoes and paddle around. Feeling the water lap your ankles and the sand between your toes will help you to become more mindful and at peace with yourself.

Go out and do some gardening – even a window box is enough to get started. You'll be rewarded with beautiful surroundings and perhaps even your own produce.

Wake up early and watch the sun rise. Take in the grandeur of the moment and step back to really appreciate the important things in your life. Allow yourself to feel at peace.

Plant a tree. Trees are critical in improving air quality and providing habitats for wildlife – you'll be doing wonders for the world!

Keep the streets tidy wherever you can. Living in a clean, litter-free area will make you and your community proud to call yourself residents. If you see some litter today, pick it up.

Attend local events. Whether it's a community celebration or an amateur sporting occasion, attending these events is usually an inexpensive way to have fun and meet new people at the same time.

57

Forgive yourself. We all make mistakes, but then we make things worse by beating ourselves up afterwards. Let go of the guilt.

58

Shop more ethically. Apps like 'Good On You' allow you to not only check how ethical a clothing store is before you shop there, but also find brands that operate more ethically.

Walk or cycle to the shops. You'll reduce the pollution caused by driving and give yourself some exercise as well.

Cut down on your meat consumption. Eating less meat has been shown to reduce the risk of multiple health problems, including cancer and heart disease – and you'll also be helping the environment.

60

61

Make your own cleaning products: for an all-purpose cleaner, mix 100 ml (½ cup) of vinegar, 50 ml (¼ cup) of baking powder and 2 litres (3 ½ pints) of water together – it's better for the environment and for your bank account!

Invest in a reusable cup. Not only will this reduce plastic waste but also many coffee shops offer money off your drinks for bringing your own cup – win-win!

62

Become a volunteer dog-walker for a charity. You'll not only enrich the dog's life by giving them an opportunity to stretch their legs, but you'll get some exercise too.

64

If you are able to take on the responsibility of a pet, consider adopting one; research shows that people with pets are happier, more trusting and less lonely than those without them.

65

Talk to your pets. You might feel strange at first, but being able to express your feelings and know you won't be judged can help your mood and mindset.

If you don't have a pet of your own, ask a friend if you can borrow theirs for a couple of hours; stroking or cuddling an animal has been proven to alleviate stress and loneliness.

Head out to your garden or a local park and soak up the sunshine. Just 10–15 minutes of sun a day can provide you with your daily recommended amount of vitamin D.

Delete some apps. Fewer apps mean fewer reasons to waste time on your devices, and it will encourage you to spend more time being present in the moment.

Identify and tackle the things that worry you. Write them down, rate them from 1–10 and take steps to eliminate them – starting from the biggest.

69

70

Learn to interpret feelings of nervousness as feelings of excitement; many successful athletes use this technique to improve their performance, but it can be applied to any situation to great effect.

Call your mother or father. For those of us who are fortunate enough to have loving parents around, there will be no one better to provide you with love and positivity. Find your supportive person.

71

72

Get to know your neighbours. There's nothing better than having friends right at your doorstep. If you need an excuse, bake a cake and take it over to share with the people next door.

73

Be genuinely happy for the achievements of those around you. It's easy to feel like someone's success is somehow your failure, but focus on just being proud of them and letting them know that.

Get inspired. Watching a motivational video, listening to an inspirational podcast or reading an uplifting book can provide you with a much-needed dose of wonder and hunger to succeed. Share these sources of inspiration with others around you to spread the positivity and amplify the good vibes.

Swallow your pride. You're only as big as what gets to you. Next time your patience is tested, be the bigger person and rise above it.

Don't sleep on an argument. Going to bed immediately after experiencing negative feelings can seriously affect your sleep and lead to very low mood. Bury the hatchet before bedtime.

Prioritise people over possessions. Our worldly things are undoubtedly important to us, but it has been proven that human relationships have more impact on our happiness than any other aspect of our lives.

78

Don't fret about the things you can't fix. All problems, almost by definition, can somehow be solved. If there's no solution, accept the situation and move on.

79

Never let anyone scare or intimidate you. Everyone is human and no one is superior to you. Remember that you are strong and you are kind, and others will respect you for it.

80

When you're feeling low, sometimes you need to treat yourself. Eating something comforting, like a dish that reminds you of happy childhood memories, can help you feel more at ease.

81

Reward yourself with a new perfume or cologne – smelling good will instantly boost your confidence and improve your mood.

82

Dress to de-stress. A great way to boost your confidence fast is by dressing in a way that makes you feel good. Put on clothes that flatter you, and face the world with a smile!

Give yourself something to look forward to. Even small treats like a piece of dark chocolate after dinner or some crisp, clean sheets on your bed can really perk you up.

83

84

Treat yourself to a manicure or pedicure – whether male or female, your hands and feet deserve some professional attention now and again.

85

Allow yourself a lazy day every once in a while. Stay in bed, watch some movies and don't feel any pressure to be productive.

86

Celebrate small victories. You don't need a big
occasion to feel proud of yourself, so celebrate the
small things just as much as the milestones.

87

Give yourself a project. It could be painting a picture or
knitting a scarf, but giving yourself something productive to work towards
will boost your mood and make you more productive!

88

Plan your day. Even listing just two to three things that
you know you want to achieve can make your day more productive,
and make you feel more accomplished when you've done them.

89

Don't overschedule your time. Feeling stressed and overwhelmed can have a very negative impact on your mood, so make sure you have broken up your tasks into manageable pieces – and be realistic about what you can do in the time that you have.

90

Take off your watch when you're on holiday. So many of us spend our lives clock-watching, so when you have the chance, enjoy the pleasures of losing track of time.

Whether you're reading your favourite book, baking cookies or playing the ukulele, spending even 15 minutes of your day doing something you enjoy will hugely improve your mood.

Look around you for small miracles, like a butterfly in flight or a flowering fruit tree; cultivating a sense of awe at the world around you encourages a positive outlook on life.

Say grace. Religious or not, being thankful for every meal you eat is a reminder of how fortunate you are. Every mouthful will taste better as a result.

94

Make a list of the places that make you feel the happiest. It could be a local beach, or a theme park or even your back garden, but note them down and visit them when you need a boost – either that, or go out and find a new happy place and share it with those closest to you.

Watch the sunset on a summer's evening. Get outside, take in the glorious light of the fading day and enjoy a precious moment of mindfulness.

95

Don't be a couch potato. Replace slobbing out on the sofa with more active pastimes, like going for a walk. You'll reap both mental and physical benefits.

Go barefoot walking or running. There are multiple benefits to walking barefoot, from better posture to less strain on your feet and joints. If it might be too risky, consider getting some barefoot shoes.

98

Wear sunscreen all year round.
Dermatologists believe that 90 per cent of visible
ageing is a result of sun damage – protect your
skin by applying a daily SPF to exposed areas.

99

Buddy up when it comes to exercise. Find a
friend who will meet up with you on a regular basis to
work out. This makes you accountable to somebody else,
so you're much less likely to wimp out and feel bad about it.

If you're tired of the gym, or find it boring, consider joining a local sports team. You'll engage your brain as well as your body – plus you'll make lots of new friends.

100

101

Get your friends together and sign up for an endurance event, such as a Tough Mudder. These combine fitness with adventure, and are a great bonding activity.

Go to a big sports game with a group of friends and feel the electricity in the atmosphere and among the crowd. The energy around you will make you feel alive.

102

Go to a gig. There's no shortage of live music these days – pick your favourite genre, find a local concert and maybe you'll discover the next big sensation.

Listen to music you enjoy when you're feeling down; the amount of dopamine released by your brain can be up to nine per cent higher when you listen to songs which remind you of good times.

Give the classics a listen. Classical music has been shown to slow your heart rate, helping you to feel more relaxed.

Work in bursts. Your brain can only focus on something
for so long before it needs a rest. Rather than kid yourself
that you can power through a full hour non-stop, try
splitting that time into three 15-minute bursts, with
a 5-minute break between each one to refresh.

Make your home a chill-out sanctuary. Dim the lights,
burn a stick of incense and play some relaxing music.
Escape from the world for a night to refresh your soul.

108

Give reiki a try. An alternative healing technique, reiki aims
to relieve pain and discomfort by balancing the body's energy centres.
Many people feel so relaxed during a session that they fall asleep!

109

Tell someone today that you love them. Partner, parent,
friend – whoever it is, tell them how much they mean to you.

110

Take a long hot shower or bath. Feel your muscles relax
in the steamy heat and take some time alone with your thoughts.

ﬁﬁ

Wear a power colour. Certain colours speak to us subconsciously and send signals to the wider world. Rich colours like red or burgundy can give you a helpful psychological boost if you associate them with success and confidence.

Look after your skin. Cleansing and moisturising your face daily will not only make you feel better, but you'll also look better, which will boost your self-esteem.

13

Sniff your way to happiness! Inhaling scents like lavender or orange zest have been shown to reduce anxiety and improve your mood.

Learn to love your body for what it can do. Remember that it isn't an ornament, but a tool and an instrument for life.

14

115

Most of us put a lot of stress on our feet or backs, and this can cause a host of problems – try reflexology to ease your muscles. Benefits include increasing your energy, boosting circulation and inducing relaxation.

116

Give daily yoga a go. This will stretch and tone your muscles. Popular poses like the plank will simultaneously work on strengthening your arms, legs, shoulders and abs.

117

Drink less alcohol. Your body and your wallet will thank you for it. You needn't stop completely, but reducing your intake gradually will pay dividends in the long run.

118

Next time you don't know what to do for the night, go to a Zumba class. It's a great cardio workout, and it's great fun – even if you've got two left feet!

119

Visualise your best self. None of us are who we want to be all the time, but imagining the 'ideal' version of ourselves can help us feel motivated.

Online discounting sites like Groupon offer great deals on fitness activities such as yoga classes, sailing or rock climbing – take advantage of these offers to try something new.

Housework can be a chore, but why not make it into a workout? The key is focusing on calorie-burning tasks like vacuuming or washing the floor – put some music on and set yourself a time limit.

Stop comparing yourself to others. You don't have to stop appreciating worth in others to do this; just remember that you are amazing in your own right.

123

Pay it forward. Next time you buy a coffee, pay a little extra to buy one for the next person. It will feel good to give somebody a nice surprise, and they might decide themselves to continue the chain of good karma.

124

Write a not-to-do list. What makes many people successful is their ability to ignore extraneous tasks that aren't important or will slow them down – cut out the things that don't matter!

125

Add just one more serving of vegetables to your meal.
By making simple changes like adding some lettuce to your sandwich or some
peas to your pasta salad, you'll be nourishing your body without even realising it.

126

When we have low serotonin levels, we tend to crave
sugar – so be careful not to binge on sugary snacks when you're
feeling low, as this can lead to a mood crash in the long run.

127

Start the day with lemon water. Hot or cold, adding lemon
to your water is great for digestion and will set you up to seize the day.

128

Listen to your body. Your body knows what it needs, but sometimes we forget to pay attention to it. Whether you're tired, hungry or feeling anxious, be aware of what your body is feeling and respond to it. Mindfulness is just one method you can use to slow down and hear what your body is trying to tell you.

If you're feeling stressed out, try drinking some beetroot juice. While it might sound odd, research has shown that just 500 ml (17 fl. oz) can reduce your blood pressure in an hour.

130

If you feel hungry, you might be thirsty! Many of us go through life dehydrated, and thirst is often mistaken for food cravings. Drink some water before you start snacking.

Try spirulina as a dietary supplement. This nutritious powder is rich in vitamins and minerals and has antioxidant and anti-inflammatory properties.

132

Remember that your mental health is just as important as your physical health. Many of us exercise regularly and eat well to stay healthy, but fewer of us take care of our minds in the same way.

Get comfortable on the sofa with your favourite childhood book – escaping to a place of comfort and familiarity will make you feel safe and warm inside.

133

134

Think about where you want to be in a year's time and make the first step towards it. Even just signing up to a sports club or going for a jog could make a big difference over time.

135

Sit down and plan the trip of a lifetime. It may not happen for years, but it will give you something amazing to work towards.

136

Try something new today, even if it's something as simple as walking down a different street on the way to work. Breaking out of your normal routine every now and then will help keep you fresh in the long run.

Embrace your emotions. It's OK to feel sad sometimes. It's good to cry as well as laugh. Don't bottle your feelings up for fear of embarrassment – share your highs and lows and let yourself feel deeply.

Create your own definition of success. It's easy to feel like you've failed at something when someone else is telling you how to win. Remember: you decide what counts.

Social media can be a powerful and addictive tool. If you find yourself feeling inadequate, remember that you are seeing somebody's highlight reel. Try to follow pages and people that promote positivity and self-love.

Visit sites like Lifefaker.com for a sense of perspective on the crazy world of social media. Never lose sight of what matters in real (rather than online) life.

Stop multitasking so much. Not only will it leave you exhausted after a prolonged time, but also research shows that the number of distractions in our modern lives may be lowering our intelligence!

142

When you're working, try to focus in 90-minute blocks with 10-minute intervals to recover. You'll get so much more done when you schedule in some downtime.

143

Even if you hate your job, try to find some enjoyment in it and always put in your best effort. You never know who might be taking notice or what might be waiting around the corner for you.

144

Take a look through all your favourite pictures and videos on your phone; reminding yourself of happy times will make you feel better in a flash.

145

Many of us keep all our photos on our phones or computers. Instead, print out your favourite pics and put them in some frames around your home so you can be surrounded by happy memories.

146

Put on your favourite cheesy song and dance around the living room with wild abandon.

Have a sing-a-long! Whether we're good at it or not, most of us love to belt out our favourite songs. Whether it's in the shower, the car or in front of the mirror with a hairbrush, hit those high notes like nobody's watching! Singing also releases endorphins, so you'll be doing it with a smile.

Whether you consider yourself artistic or not, get a canvas, a brush and some paints and get creative! Express yourself freely without fear of criticism or judgement.

148

149

You may not consider yourself a poet, but try to write a poem. It doesn't have to be a masterpiece, but it may help you to express your feelings in an imaginative and rewarding way.

Make a playlist of all the songs that make you want to jump around and sing along, and play it whenever you're in need of a boost.

150

151

Keep some of your favourite poems, quotes and snippets of writing close to hand, so that you can refer to them whenever you need a pick-me-up.

Create a happiness box. Whether it's a shoebox or a bedside drawer, write down special moments and happy memories on bits of paper and open the box whenever you're feeling down.

152

153

Studies have shown that people tend to feel happier around
the colours of sunshine and spring fields – consider transforming
a space in your home to bring the outside in.

154

Eat more omega-3s in foods like oily fish, avocados,
walnuts and chia seeds. Eating these essential fatty acids can promote
a healthy heart and mind, as well as improving your mood.

155

Make Brazil nuts part of your diet; they contain selenium –
if your body has low levels of this antioxidant, your mood can dip.
Try baking them into cookies or nibbling them just as they are.

156

Act like today is the best day of your life.
You will feel the way you behave and your positivity
will affect those around you as well.

157

Chew some gum – the repetitive action of gnawing
on gum can promote relaxation and reduce stress.

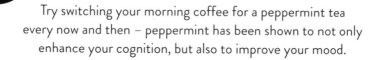

158

Try switching your morning coffee for a peppermint tea
every now and then – peppermint has been shown to not only
enhance your cognition, but also to improve your mood.

159

Host a coffee morning. Get everyone to bring along a cake and make sure you've got enough tea and coffee to go around – you can get to know new people as well as raising money for a good cause.

Host a charity sale to get rid of unwanted clutter and raise money for a worthy cause.

Be generous. This doesn't mean spending money: donate your time. Helping someone move house or listening to a relative's worries can be a priceless gift.

161

162

Organise a date night. It can be with your partner or even one of your friends, but find a couple of hours to spend some quality time together.

Keep your friends close. Relationships not only bring joy to our lives, but they also help us to delay our mental and physical decline and are good predictors of long, happy lives.

163

164

Be more optimistic. Keeping a positive outlook will not only make you a happier person, but optimism is also good for your health. In a study, researchers in the US found that optimists were 76 per cent more likely to have good health scores and a healthier weight; being healthier will in turn make you happier, and so the cycle will continue!

165

See failure as a new start. Failure is not the end, it's just a chance to do something better; by starting with a fresh perspective, you might achieve something even more amazing.

166

Don't be a pessimist. Pessimism makes us shy away from new experiences, and leaves us scared of failure. By taking more chances and being more positive, you never know what you might achieve.

167

Remember that you have a choice. Whatever decisions you are making and however tough they may seem, keep your options in mind.

168

Actively seek feedback. It may be hard to hear at times, but by seeking constructive criticism and advice, you'll have the guidance needed to become the best version of yourself.

Realise you can do anything. The only limit to your capabilities is yourself, and if you believe you can do something, you're far more likely to be able to do it.

169

Saying no can be difficult sometimes, but it's important to prioritise your own well-being. Refuse invitations that you know won't make you happy and devote that time to self-care.

Let go of your grudges – they can take up so much of your energy that it's best to have a productive conversation about the issue.

Many of us are happy to buy expensive gifts for our friends, but we scrimp when it comes to ourselves. Treat yourself occasionally to something you wouldn't normally splash out on.

173

Focus on your inner scorecard. You are in competition only with yourself, not everyone around you.

174

Find people who share your outlook on life and have deep and meaningful conversations with them. However, don't automatically shut out those who disagree with you – it's important to be challenged in a healthy debate sometimes.

175

Smile at people. It's simple, it's free and it could really brighten up someone else's day – as well as your own.

176

Talk to someone! Whether it's face to face,
on the phone or via video call, connecting with other
people and hearing about a world that's bigger than
your own will make you feel connected and content.

177

**Hug someone. Even a quick hug with
a friend or an acquaintance can decrease
stress levels and improve our health.**

Try writing your negative thoughts and your worries on pieces of paper before throwing them away. Studies show that physically throwing away your worries can lessen their hold on you.

178

179

If you're going through a tough spot, start making a list of reasons why it was worth getting out of bed today and why you should persevere. Focus on the positives.

Leave affirming messages around your home. You'll feel a burst of positivity whenever you find one.

180

181

Make sure you have an appetising breakfast to look forward to in the morning. It could be your favourite cereal, fruit or some overnight oats. As your first meal of the day, not only will this put you in a good mood, but it will also replenish your body's glucose supply and provide essential nutrients.

182

Eat within two hours of waking up. Breakfast-lover or not, try to eat something in this window after sleep to see significant boosts to your mood and concentration.

183

Consider swapping your morning coffee
with an apple; while there's no caffeine kick, an apple
can fuel your body, help stabilise your blood sugar, and
the fibre it contains will keep you fuller for longer.

184

Take the stress out of your week by making
lunches in bulk at the weekend; you'll also be
more likely to stick to a healthy diet by removing
the temptation to buy something unsuitable.

185

Make your bed. It takes a couple of minutes but will set you up for an organised day. Plus you'll thank yourself when you return home in the evening.

186

Prepare an amazing outfit for yourself. Clothing can do wonders for confidence, and by lining up an outfit the night before you wear it, you can also remove those last-minute stresses.

Watch kitten or puppy videos. Do you even need telling that these are an instant mood-lifter? Countless heart-warming clips are but a click away.

187

188

Make yourself a healthy snack selection. Having a range of healthy snacks to hand when you're hungry will stop you from picking high-calorie, high-sugar snacks at short notice.

Grow your own! Not only will this bring greater life to your garden (or your window box), but you'll also realise how much better food tastes when you grow it yourself.

189

90

Reduce food waste. Food waste ends up in landfill, where it releases CO_2 into the atmosphere. By buying only what you need and using up your food creatively you'll be saving money as well as the planet!

91

Learn what's seasonal. B which fruits and vegetab seasonal throughout the become a more responsi and you'll also know whe your produce to get the

192

Share your food. A great way to reduce your food waste is with apps like 'Olio'. These apps allow shops and individuals to save food which would otherwise be thrown away; plus it's a money-saver.

193

Compost your waste. Composting has a multitude of benefits, including reducing greenhouse gas production, improving soil quality and saving you money on fertiliser.

194

Try to reduce your plastic waste. By making simple changes like buying a reusable water bottle and choosing products without plastic wrapping, you'll be making a positive change for the benefit of the environment.

195

Turn electricals off when they're not in use.
By doing this, you'll not only save money on
your energy bills, but you'll also be reducing
your negative impact on the environment.

196

Get yourself a tote bag. Tote bags are always
useful and will help you reduce the amount of
plastic bags you need when you shop – get one
with a cool design and you'll never look back.

Fix it, don't throw it! Repairing and recycling your clothes and items can save you loads of money on replacing things, and it will help the environment too.

Invest! Apps like 'Moneybox' help you manage your finances by rounding up your purchases and investing your spare change. It all adds up in the long run, and you'll be saving without even realising.

Shop around for cheap alternatives to your usual staples. Studies have proved that many of us can't identify our favourite brands without their usual packaging – you never know how much you could save.

200

Exercise anywhere. Getting a little extra movement into the day can be simple. For instance, if you're cooking dinner, do some standing push-ups while you wait for a pot to boil. Stand about an arm's length from the kitchen counter, and push your arms against the counter – push in and out to tone your arms and shoulders.

Make a list of things you love about yourself that doesn't include your appearance (even if you love the way you look). Keep adding to it, and reminding yourself how wonderful you are.

201

202

Make a blanket fort for yourself with pillows and throws. Hide away with a book or a movie, and some of your favourite snacks.

Give yourself and your friends a spa day, but at home. Get face masks, nail varnish and scented candles, and get pampering!

203

204

Go out for a bike ride – it's the perfect
aerobic, cardiovascular activity that lets you
enjoy the beautiful scenery around you and
allows you to explore your local area.

205

Suggest to your friends that you all go out dancing;
it's an incredible cardio workout and you'll burn
a load of calories without even realising it.

206

Gather your friends and head to the bowling alley. Studies show that during a three-game series the average person walks more than half a mile.

207

Invite your friends over for a movie marathon – complete with pyjamas and popcorn – and get lost in your favourite films.

208

Go to an escape room. Gather a group of friends and test your problem-solving skills by trying to get out in the time allowed – you're bound to have a laugh!

209

If you live near the sea, get out and paddleboard – not only does this activity get you out in the sea air, but it's also great for balance and core strength and it's a low-impact full-body workout.

210

Spend time with your favourite people. Research suggests that you are the average of the five people you spend the most time with, so make sure those five are the best people you know!

211

Have a photoshoot. Whether it's professional or amateur,
alone or with family and friends, capturing moments and memories will give you
something special to look back on in months and years to come.

212

Take a selfie. In public or in private, take a picture of
yourself when you're feeling good. Studies show that this can boost
your confidence and make you feel better about yourself.

213

Make a time capsule for yourself or your relatives – it'll be
like a present for your future self or maybe your descendants.

214

Take on a home improvement project;
this will give you something to focus on in
your spare time and at the end you'll have
something useful or beautiful to show for it.

215

Leave a note. Most notes are requests or
complaints. Instead, leave a funny message on
a colleague's desk or a heartfelt declaration on
the bathroom mirror for a loved one to find.

216

Keep on top of your inbox. Many of us are constantly bombarded by emails and spam. By staying in control of your inbox and filtering it regularly, you'll feel less overwhelmed on a daily basis.

217

Don't pay attention to what others are doing. You are on your own course in life and will achieve the goals that are important to you.

218

Set an intention for your day. When you wake up, give yourself a positive intention such as 'I'm going to be productive'. This will set the right tone for the day ahead.

Take a walk before you eat lunch. In the middle of the day there is normally a natural lull in your circadian rhythm, which can make you feel drowsy. Get some sunshine and fresh air to perk you up.

219

220

Stop snoozing your alarm – it will only make you more tired and you'll get more done if you get up when you're supposed to.

Run yourself a hot bath with your favourite bath products – lavender oil, bath salts and scented candles are perfect additions for the ultimate relaxation experience.

221

Train your brain. By doing puzzles regularly, like sudoku or crosswords, you'll keep your brain in good shape. What's more, studies have shown that completing a crossword releases a decent amount of dopamine. It's certainly worth a try.

223

Find a place near you that allows a clear view of the night sky; lie back with a friend and stargaze for as long as you can.

224

Master a martial art. With a variety of options to choose from – whether it's karate, judo or Brazilian jiujitsu – martial arts are a great way to keep fit, stay disciplined and learn self-defence.

Spend some time with younger nieces, nephews or a friend's children. Kids are all about being silly and having fun, and their infectious energy is bound to rub off on you.

Listen to a podcast. There are plenty of options freely available out there – they'll keep you entertained while you're cleaning, out for a walk or cooking dinner.

Go to the theatre. A cultural activity which has been around since ancient times, going to the theatre can be a truly cathartic or escapist experience – and it beats TV any day.

Jump on a train and go somewhere you've never been before – you never know what kind of new and exciting places you might find along the way.

229

Do the thing you least want to do today first. Once it's over and out the way, the rest of your day will be a breeze by comparison.

Breathe! Look out for abnormal patterns in your breathing. When we're stressed or anxious our breathing can be rapid and shallow – slow down and take deep breaths to feel better.

231

If you've had a rough day, watch your favourite comedian or your favourite comedy sketches. Laughter will lift your spirits and your mood in no time.

232

Put your phone away during mealtimes. Agree with your dining companions to put your phones out of reach for the duration of your meal. The pleasure of real, uninterrupted conversation will be greater by far.

233

Find your lucky charm. Plenty of studies have shown the effectiveness of placebos, so find yourself something like a key ring or bracelet that gives you good vibes and take it with you wherever you go.

234

Stay open-minded. Don't close your mind to arguments and ideas that you don't agree with – have reasoned debates and discussions, and seek to understand others with different opinions.

235

Many of us are quick to complain, but not many of us give praise to those around us. Take the time to give compliments to those who serve and help you; the positivity will come back around.

Remember how precious your time is. No one looks back on their life and fondly remembers the nights they stayed late at the office. While it's important to work hard, make sure you live life to the full when you're off the clock.

236

Organise social events at work. It could be anything from lunch to team sports or a karaoke night. Feeling closer to your colleagues will make a huge difference to your mood on a daily basis.

Visit a museum. Small and local or vast and further afield, they're often free or inexpensive and provide a whole day's worth of fascination.

Let go of a short-term mindset. Not every improvement will happen immediately. Stick to your plans and let progress creep up on you.

240

Start a diary. You can pour out your feelings, hopes and fears in words, without fear of judgement. The practice of recording and reflecting on your experiences is good for your mental health, plus looking back on previous entries can give you valuable perspective on how far you've come.

241

If you work or study above the ground floor and tend to take the lift or escalator, try taking the stairs. It's a small change that could make a big difference to the amount of exercise you do.

Get more vitamin C. Studies show that this vitamin has natural anti-depressant properties. Oranges, peppers and leafy greens are good sources.

242

243

Swim! Whether it's in a pool or the sea, get your swimming gear on and dive in – not only will it strengthen your muscles and your heart, but it will also build up your endurance.

List the things you've done throughout your life that make you feel most proud – be sure to look at the list whenever you're lacking confidence. Relive those experiences in your mind. Feels amazing, right?

244

245

A low GI (glycaemic index) diet can have multiple health benefits, such as steadier energy levels, less bloating and fewer sugar cravings. Look into adding low GI foods to your diet.

246

Don't skip a meal. If you don't eat, your blood sugar sinks and sends stress signals to your brain. If you really don't have time to eat something substantial, have snacks on hand to nibble.

Grow some herbs at home – not only will it add a touch of colour to your living space, but having fresh herbs readily available will also encourage you to cook healthy and tasty meals.

247

248

Get a change of scene. Sometimes your current mood can become associated with a particular place. It's surprising how easily new surroundings can refresh your outlook.

Take on a new challenge. It can be anything from running a mile to writing a novel, but whatever you choose, enjoy the process and celebrate your progress along the way.

249

250

Book a holiday. Whether it's abroad or closer to home, for a fortnight or just the weekend, get something in your diary that you can look forward to for an ongoing boost to your mood.

251

Take yourself on a date. You don't have to wait for someone else to take you out – buy yourself flowers and do something you love to do. Spend some quality time with yourself. You deserve it!

252

Get engrossed in a good TV show. Sometimes there is nothing better than a series that grips you from start to finish – and there are so many good ones out there.

253

Try sleeping in the buff. It might seem odd, but sleeping naked has multiple benefits for your comfort and circulation. Good-quality sleep also produces melatonin, which has anti-ageing benefits.

254

If it's a cold day, don't hide away indoors. Wrap up warm, grab a flask of something hot and head outside – the fresh air will do wonders for your mood.

255

If you tend to feel lower in the winter, it may be due to seasonal affective disorder (SAD). Get as much sunlight as you can, or look into light therapy to brighten your mood.

Zoom out. A great technique for putting any problems into perspective is to mentally zoom out from it. Will what's troubling you now matter in a week, a month, a year?

256

257

Eat chia seeds. As one of the most
nutrient-dense foods on the planet, chia seeds
are great for a healthy body and mind.

258

Put some garlic in your food. Garlic contains
allicin, a bioactive compound which has a range of
benefits including improved immune function – though
you may need some breath mints after a big helping!

Drink some herbal tea. Sage tea in particular has been shown to improve mood, mental function and memory in healthy adults.

259

260

In studies, hibiscus tea has been shown to reduce stress over a period of time – try drinking some at work or before bed to see long-term changes in your mood.

Eat some probiotic-rich foods like natural yogurt. These have been shown to improve gut health and leave you feeling lighter – grab a spoon!

261

Eat more slowly. Taking time over your food can lead to better digestion, better hydration, easier weight loss or maintenance, and greater satisfaction with your meals.

262

263

Don't starve yourself. There's little science to support 'detox' diets or 'juice cleanses'. Try to make better – not necessarily fewer – food choices.

Munch on mangoes. With antioxidant properties that protect against cancers, mangoes are also great for your skin, eye health and digestion. This delicious, versatile fruit will make you feel great.

264

Give veganism a go. Despite common misconceptions, an ethical plant-based, cruelty-free diet is a great way to nourish your body, control your weight and nurture your soul.

Stop dieting. If you find yourself constantly going from one diet to another and failing, try to focus on changing your lifestyle. A healthier way of life will be far more sustainable.

267

Load up on fruit and vegetables. A key study recently found that eating just one extra portion of fruit and veg a day could cut your risk of an early death from any cause by 20 per cent.

268

Go easy on the sweets. Instead of eating candy, try munching on chocolate-coated nuts or fruits. They're just as tasty, but won't have as many crazy ingredients as the alternative.

269

Cut down on fizzy drinks. Whether you drink regular or diet fizzy drinks, they all contain chemicals that can affect how you feel. Try mixing fruit juice with sparkling water for a purer form of refreshment.

270

There's no need to deny yourself an occasional sweet treat, but choosing the right snack to keep you going can be tricky – try whipping up some no-bake energy bites with rolled oats, dates, honey, nuts and peanut butter for a healthier treat.

271

Eat raw. Food that grows out of the ground is infinitely better for you than processed stuff that comes in packets. Next time you get peckish, try snacking on carrots, peppers or celery.

272

Embrace the power of asking for what you want. Whether it's a date or a pay rise, the worst that can happen is that you get a no.

273

Meet your match(a). Matcha tea is a naturally bright green drink containing L-theanine, which promotes the production of dopamine and serotonin, boosting your memory, concentration and mood.

274

Buy local. You'll feel closer to your community when you support businesses in your area – farmers' markets are a great place to start.

Simply getting outside with a friend to play catch or throw around a Frisbee are simple but joyous ways to spend a few hours. Plus, the fresh air will do you wonders.

275

Play a board game. Whether it's *Monopoly* or *Trivial Pursuit*, these games will bring your friends or family together – as long as you don't get into any arguments!

Play fetch with a dog. Whether it's your own pooch or one you've borrowed from a friend, no one can feel sad when they're watching a dog having the time of their life!

Try F45. This intense Australian workout programme is a team-based exercise that focuses on motivation, innovation and results. Every workout is unique, and it's a total-body experience that will leave you feeling great.

279

Talk to strangers. You might make a friend, learn
something new from them or at the very least have
a good story to tell about your experience.

280

Settle old feuds. If you've had an argument with a friend
or relative and you no longer talk to them, try making
things right between you. You'll feel a huge weight taken
off your shoulders when you've put the past behind you.

281

Surround yourself with shades of blue. The soothing
hue of the sky and sea is naturally calming.

282

Go out to a flower garden or buy some for your home. Studies
show that flowers provide an instant and lasting mood boost.

283

Go to an art exhibition. You don't have to be an expert to enjoy it – form your own opinions. You might even be inspired to make some art yourself!

284

Sign up to be an organ donor. The process is usually quick and easy, and you'll be committing to an amazing and selfless gift for others.

285

Apps like 'Charity Miles' donate money for every mile you run, jog or cycle; since altruism has been proven to release endorphins, why not double your exercise high!

286

Stretching is good for both body and mind. Studies have shown that stretching can not only leave the body feeling more supple, but can even improve your mental health in both the short and long term.

287

Stand tall. Our posture can influence how we feel inside, so straighten up and walk like a total boss.

288

Track your health. There are now more ways than ever to keep track of your health. Pedometers, Fitbits and apps like 'MyFitnessPal' are easy ways to track your diet, exercise or even your mood over time.

289

Make more eye contact. This makes you appear more confident and charismatic to those around, and you'll find yourself having better conversations and meetings.

290

It's important to stay current, but sometimes the news can get us down; try reading good news websites like www.goodnewsnetwork.org and www.positive.news to feel more positive about the world.

291

Start a blog. You can discuss your life, your hobbies or maybe even your favourite recipes. Sharing your passions in this way will boost your self-esteem.

292

Take an evening class. Learning something new is a great way to keep your mind agile, plus you'll come into contact with like-minded people.

Dress up for yourself. You don't have to save your favourite garments for special occasions: every day of your life is a special occasion.

293

294

Retail therapy may not be a long-term fix, but it can certainly boost your mood in the moment! Treat yourself to a shopping trip every now and then.

It might sound weird, but studies have shown that sniffing a romantic partner's clothes or pillow can reduce your body's levels of the stress hormone cortisol. See if it soothes you.

295

296

Put on something bold and make a statement. It could be a shiny accessory or a new pair of shoes – your confidence will shine through whatever you're wearing.

297

Buy some weights and use them at home. You don't need to join a gym for a workout – by looking up exercises online and having weights at hand, you can work out while doing housework or even watching TV.

298

Play crazy golf. A game for all ages, crazy golf is a great way to spend some time outside with friends and family – after all, you can't possibly be sad when putting a ball through a miniature moving windmill or a plastic tiger.

299

Try some t'ai chi. Although this Chinese discipline is slow and gentle, it addresses the key components of fitness, including muscle strength, flexibility and balance.

300

Write a letter to your future self. Say where you are and where you hope you'll be when you open it. Expressing your dreams and desires will encourage you to make them real.

301

Get out some pencils and start sketching. Even if you don't think you can draw, artistic activities can promote positive thoughts and make you feel at ease – many people find that art makes them more optimistic.

302

Stuck in a rut? Read the autobiographies or biographies of the people who inspire you; learning about their struggles and their path to success will give you a positive outlook on your own future.

Go to the library. The simple pleasures of a book cannot be beaten. Surround yourself with knowledge and take some time out to enjoy your favourite genre.

303

304

Relive your best memory. When you're feeling down, remember that time in your life when you felt blissfully happy. Conjure up every small detail and try to feel those happy emotions again.

305

Learn more about yourself by taking a personality test. It may not be totally accurate, but answering the questions will help you to assess yourself and might give you ideas for self-improvement.

Try an online quiz. Pick something as silly as you like – sites like Buzzfeed and Sporcle offer some great, bizarre quizzes that will see you smiling in no time.

306

307

Watch a sad movie and let the tears flow. Releasing
your emotions will relieve any built-up tension
and lift your spirits in the long run.

308

Create positive or inspirational reminders on your phone's
calendar for weeks or months ahead. You'll then get messages
out of the blue to make you smile when you least expect it.

309

Paint your own postcard and send it. Create your masterpiece with some simple acrylic paints, and pen a sweet message on the back to someone special. The personal touch will leave everyone smiling.

310

Memorise your favourite poems. This is beneficial for your overall brain function and capability, and you'll feel amazing knowing that you can summon some classic lines from memory.

311

Leave a copy of a good book in a cafe for someone else to find and enjoy. You'll feel great knowing that you might brighten someone else's day.

312

Make a Pinterest board. Fill it with your favourite recipes, décor ideas or design projects to give you inspiration and delight next time you need to be uplifted.

313

Get yourself a vanilla-scented candle. Studies have shown that the scent of the vanilla bean can lift your mood and have a major effect on your happiness levels.

314

Write a love letter. You don't even have to send it, but getting your feelings out and being as soppy as you like will make you feel more loveable yourself.

315

Pray. Whether or not you're religious, lose yourself in a moment of deep contemplation and allow your words to come honestly and from the heart. It can bring great joy and comfort.

316

Keep a promise. By doing something you've agreed to do, you'll feel more honest, reliable and proud of the person you are.

Read a positive lifestyle book – this one is an excellent place to start! If you find yourself feeling low, pick up a book that will offer you advice on a better mood. You're bound to learn something from it.

318

Practise what you preach. It's easy to give advice to those around you, but make sure you follow your own suggestions once in a while. If you wish success on your friends, wish it for yourself too.

319

Look at others without judging them. We're all guilty of it, but if you can stop yourself making judgements the negativity in your mind will stop and you'll start seeing the positives in others and in yourself as well.

Step back from silly arguments. It's easy to get caught up in the moment and fall out over small things, but try to take a moment to think and ask yourself if it's worth the pain.

320

321

Reconnect with an old friend. Often we drift away from friends when life takes us in different directions, but rekindling a past friendship can be an extremely rewarding and positive journey.

Be tolerant of others. Not everyone can get on, but focus on respecting people's differences and seeking to understand them. By removing this negativity from your life, you'll find yourself feeling much happier.

322

Focus on experiences, not things. We may all dream of having certain luxury items, but a recent survey found that those who have luxury cars are no happier than those with shabby ones.

323

324

If you're struggling not to overspend, money-saving apps can give you a helping hand. Try downloading one to get insights into how you spend and how you can save.

Use a different search engine. Browser extensions like Ecosia use the ad revenue from your searches to plant trees where they're needed most.

325

Have an opposite day. Using your non-dominant
hand to perform tasks can build new connections
in your brain, boosting your cognitive agility –
as well as adding some fun to mundane tasks.

327

If you struggle to put away your devices before bed,
try installing f.lux software; f.lux softens and warms the
lighting of your phone, tablet or computer to remove
the blue light which interferes with your body clock.

328

Go to sleep when you feel tired! It's easy to get distracted
and stay up late in the evenings, but when you feel sleepy,
let your body and mind have a well-earned rest.

Listen to birdsong. It's all around most of us and can set us up naturally for the day ahead.

329

330

Read an uplifting poem such as 'Laughing Song' by William Blake or 'One of These Days' by James W. Foley.

Try putting an ylang-ylang-fragranced diffuser in your home. This scent is known to alleviate nervous afflictions, stress, anger and anxiety while inducing a relaxing feeling.

331

Listen to 'Weightless' by Marconi Union. Studies have shown that it is more relaxing than other ambient tracks and it reduces overall anxiety by a significant amount.

332

333

Brush your teeth, and wash your hands and face. Just by cleaning a few parts of your body, carefully and mindfully, you'll feel reinvigorated and more relaxed.

Clean your nose. It may seem odd, but having a blocked nose can leave you feeling tired and irritable; try cleaning your nasal passages with saline solution.

334

335

Say yes to new adventures. Even if it's not something you would normally do, you never know where things might lead – so say yes to opportunities to broaden your horizons or engage with new people.

336

Don't shy away from the rain. Get outside and jump in the puddles, feeling the drops on your skin. There'll be no greater joy than the blankets, dry clothes and hot drinks when you return home.

If you're feeling low, take a brisk walk. Studies have shown that without any other lifestyle change, just taking a 30-minute walk a day can make a huge difference to your mood and your physical health.

337

338

Spend an hour or so by a river. Not only are you getting fresh air, but the flowing water and the light reflected on it is also perfect for calming your thoughts.

339

Write a fan letter. If an artist, musician or writer means something to you, tell them. You might not get a reply, but you will be adding positivity to the world.

340

Play a card game. This is a classic pastime, fun for all ages, and studies have shown that card games are beneficial for motor skills and cognitive health.

341

Send a funny or silly message. Brighten someone else's day by sending them a text or an email that you know will make them smile.

342

Set yourself a fundraising challenge. Be it a sponsored walk, swim or read-a-thon, sites like GoFundMe and JustGiving make it easier than ever to raise money for causes dear to your heart.

343

Track your progress. A great way to feel amazing is to set yourself fitness targets and work towards them. When you reach them, set new ones to stay motivated.

344

Ice cream is delicious, but the spike to your blood sugar can affect your mood. Try fruity frozen yogurt or frozen bananas with dark chocolate as a healthier, mood-boosting alternative.

345

Bake a cake. Cooking and baking is a great form of therapy, and has been shown to help reduce stress, as well as curing boredom, insomnia and anxiety. Plus you get some tasty treats at the end – win-win!

346

Become a better listener. In conversation, often we just wait for our turn to talk without really paying attention to what the other person is saying. Try saying less and listening more: it will make you a better friend, colleague, partner or parent.

347

Embrace childlike wonder. When children look around, they are fascinated and curious about whatever they see. Keep this in mind and feel a sense of awe at the world around you.

348

Observe those around you. By analysing what it is that makes other people seem engaging and confident, you'll discover how you can adopt these traits yourself. Your confidence will shine.

349

Start before you feel ready. Sometimes it's too easy to wait for the 'perfect' moment, but this may never come. Get started as soon as possible and see what you're capable of.

350

Make the appointment. It's easy to put things off like going to a doctor or a therapist, but by seeking professional advice you'll be taking a positive step to address whatever issue is troubling you.

Be humble. Confidence is important, but arrogance is unpleasant. Studies show that being humble reduces anxiety, enhances self-control and makes individuals more generous.

If you're worried about something you have to do, visualise the situation going well beforehand. When you expect success, you're more likely to get it.

352

353

It's not failure; it's a learning experience. If something doesn't quite go as planned, try to learn from it and move on – don't dwell on things that can't be changed.

Keep your home tidy. As obvious as it sounds, mess will affect your mood, not just your ability to find whatever you're looking for.

354

355

Stop piling on the pressure. Often good things happen when we stop searching for them, so try worrying less about pursuing happiness and let it find you.

Appreciate beauty. Find the majesty in the people, buildings and landscapes around you. Take a sketchbook with you to capture something of their unique appeal.

356

357

Save money with minimal effort. Browser extensions like Honey automatically find and apply coupon codes at online checkouts with a single click. You'll feel great once you've bagged a bargain.

358

Set deadlines. If you have something you need to complete, set yourself a deadline a couple of days before that. Even if you don't quite meet it, you should be on time for the real thing.

359

Have a nap. A short nap of 20–30 minutes can offer you significant benefits for alertness and performance, without leaving you feeling groggy or lying awake at night.

Try rosehip oil. Rosehip oil is a great natural moisturiser
and has many other benefits for your skin; it has
also been known to even out skin tone and reduce
the appearance of wrinkles and skin damage.

361

Fight for a cause. Find something you're passionate about and get involved. Whether it's joining Amnesty International to defend human rights or volunteering your time to help underprivileged kids in your community, being selflessly part of something bigger is as laudable as it is rewarding.

362

Playing strategy games like chess and mah-jong makes for an excellent brain workout. Studies have shown that complex games can improve academic performance and prevent neural decline.

363

Try using Dead Sea salt; this natural substance has been shown to relieve skin ailments, and its minerals can also help your skin retain moisture.

364

Compliment yourself. No need to wait for anyone else. Find a mirror, look yourself in the eye and give credit where it's most certainly due.

Eat dark chocolate! Most of us crave chocolate when we're feeling down – and for good reason! Chocolate contains tryptophan, which has mood-boosting effects. One study found that the taste, texture and even the smell of chocolate makes us happy.

If you're interested in finding out more about our books, find us on Facebook at **Summersdale Publishers** and follow us on Twitter at **@Summersdale**.

www.summersdale.com